QUEEN ELIZABETH HALL, LONDON

International Security Conference

I'M OFTEN ASKED WHICH IS THE MOST DANGEROUS *TERRORIST GROUP* IN THE WORLD.

AND FROM MY TIME IN THE *SAS*, I CAN TELL YOU THE ANSWER IS *NOT* WHAT YOU MIGHT EXPECT...

MAX WEBBER, SECURITY CONSULTANT

...BUT I CAN ALSO ASSURE YOU, IT *IS* A GROUP YOU SHOULD *FEAR*.

KLIK!

FORCE THREE

LET ME TELL YOU ABOUT THEM.

FORCE THREE DON'T CALL THEMSELVES TERRORISTS. THEY IDENTIFY AS *ECO-WARRIORS*, FIGHTING TO PROTECT THE EARTH – PLANET NUMBER *THREE* IN THE SOLAR SYSTEM – FROM POLLUTION.

THEY'RE OPPOSED TO CLIMATE CHANGE, RAINFOREST DESTRUCTION, NUCLEAR POWER, GENETIC ENGINEERING – AN AGENDA SIMILAR TO *GREENPEACE*.

THE DIFFERENCE IS, FORCE THREE ARE *FANATICS*. THEY WILL *KILL* ANYONE WHO GETS IN THEIR WAY.

THIS IS *KASPAR*, THEIR LEADER. AS YOU CAN SEE, HE CARES ABOUT THE PLANET SO MUCH, IT'S GONE TO HIS *HEAD!*

KASPAR MAY *LOOK* SILLY BUT HE'S PLANTED *BOMBS* IN SIX COUNTRIES, DESTROYED A *CAR FACTORY* IN DETROIT AND *ASSASSINATED* THE GERMAN JOURNALIST MARJORIE SCHULTZ AFTER SHE *CRITICIZED* FORCE THREE.

FORCE THREE GROW MORE SERIOUS AND DEADLY WITH EVERY PASSING DAY.

IN MY VIEW, KASPAR IS *THE MOST DANGEROUS MAN ALIVE.*

ALEX RIDER

ARK ANGEL

THE GRAPHIC NOVEL

ANTHONY HOROWITZ

Antony Johnston • Amrit Birdi

WALKER

First published 2020 by Walker Books Ltd
87 Vauxhall Walk, London SE11 5HJ

2 4 6 8 10 9 7 5 3 1

Text and illustrations © 2020 Walker Books Ltd
Based on the original novel *Ark Angel* © 2005 Stormbreaker Productions Ltd
Adapted by Antony Johnston
Illustrations by Amrit Birdi & Co. Ltd

Anthony Horowitz has asserted his moral rights

Trademarks © 2020 Stormbreaker Productions Ltd
Alex Rider™, Boy with Torch Logo™

This book has been typeset in Wild Words and Serpentine Bold

Printed in China

British Library Cataloguing in Publication Data:
a catalogue record for this book is available
from the British Library

ISBN 978-1-4063-4189-8

www.walker.co.uk

...*FORCE THREE* TODAY CLAIMED RESPONSIBILITY FOR KILLING *MAX WEBBER*, AND SAID THEIR NEXT TARGET WOULD BE *"SOMETHING THE WORLD WOULD NEVER FORGET"*...

ST DOMINIC'S PRIVATE HOSPITAL, LONDON

HELLO, *ALEX.*

OH, HI, *PAUL.* HOW ARE YOU DOING?

I'M OK, I GUESS. THE NURSE SAID *THIS* ARRIVED FOR YOU THIS MORNING.

FUNNY, THERE'S NO MESSAGE INSIDE...

ALEX! VERY SORRY TO HEAR YOU WERE HURT, OLD CHAP. GET WELL SOON AND TAKE IT EASY!

BY THE WAY, THIS CARD WILL *SELF-DESTRUCT* IN FIVE SECONDS.

OH!

HEH! GOOD OLD **SMITHERS**...

YOU'VE GOT **STRANGE** FRIENDS. IS IT TRUE YOU'RE GOING **HOME** TOMORROW?

YEAH. WHAT ABOUT YOU? I DON'T EVEN KNOW WHERE YOU LIVE. YOU'VE MENTIONED **LONDON, MOSCOW, NEW YORK, FRANCE**... WHERE DO YOU ACTUALLY GO TO SCHOOL?

I DON'T, I HAVE **TUTORS**. MY LIFE'S SORT OF WEIRD, BECAUSE OF ... MY **DAD** ... AND EVERYTHING, REALLY.

ANYWAY, I'M JUST **JEALOUS** OF YOU GETTING OUT OF HERE.

GOODNIGHT, ALEX.

THERE'S CONOR, THE *NIGHT RECEPTIONIST*. MAYBE HE'LL LET ME STAND OUTSIDE, JUST FOR A FEW MINUTES...

HI! WE'RE HERE TO VISIT *PAUL DREVIN*. CAN YOU TELL US WHAT ROOM HE'S IN?

LITTLE *LATE* FOR VISITING, ISN'T IT? ANYWAY, I *CAN'T* DISCLOSE THAT INFORMATION WITHOUT...

...AUTHORIZATION.

SECOND FLOOR. ROOM EIGHT.

KCHK!

THAT WON'T FOOL THEM FOR **LONG**, THOUGH. I HAVE TO DRAW THEM **AWAY** FROM PAUL.

THERE'S THE ROOM. LOOKS **EMPTY**...

I'VE GOT TO TIME IT RIGHT AND **MAKE** THEM COME AFTER ME!

W-WHO ARE **YOU**? I JUST WENT TO THE TOILET...

PAUL DREVIN?

AFTER HIM!

YOU HAVE TO COME WITH US.

NOW.

WHAT WAS THAT? I HEARD *SCREAMING*...

WUMP!

THAT'S THE ELEMENT OF *SURPRISE* GONE. NOW THE OTHERS WILL KNOW I'M DANGEROUS. BUT I HAVE TO KEEP THEM AWAY FROM THE REAL PAUL!

PHYSIOTHERAPY

COME ON, PAUL, THERE'S NOWHERE TO GO! WE JUST WANT TO TALK.

JUST A NICE, FRIENDLY TALK. YOU, ME AND MY *FP9*...

OHHH ... MY HEAD...

I **HATE** GETTING KNOCKED OUT. STILL, I SUPPOSE IT'S BETTER THAN THE **ALTERNATIVE**.

NOW... WHAT HAVE YOU GOT YOURSELF INTO **THIS** TIME, ALEX?

HORNCHURCH TOWERS

AND WHY WOULD **ARMED MEN** COME FOR PAUL DREVIN? WHO IS HE? AND WHY DOES HIS **NAME** SOUND FAMILIAR...?

OH, OF COURSE! NOT PAUL — **NIKOLEI DREVIN**, THE RUSSIAN BILLIONAIRE! THAT MUST BE HIS FATHER!

THE **BOSS** WANTS TO SEE YOU.

YOU MEAN YOU **GENIUSES** AREN'T IN CHARGE?

NO ONE LIKES A SMART-ARSE, PAUL.

MOVE.

HELLO, PAUL.

YOU'VE CAUSED US A **GREAT** DEAL OF ANNOYANCE. BUT LET ME INTRODUCE MYSELF. I AM THE **LEADER** OF FORCE THREE...

...MY NAME IS **KASPAR**.

HAVE YOU HEARD OF ME?

DESPITE YOUR JOKE, I CAN SEE YOU ARE *SURPRISED* BY MY APPEARANCE.

YOU MAY THINK IT'S *EXTREME*. BUT IT REPRESENTS WHO I AM, AND WHAT I *BELIEVE*. WE ARE ALL PART OF THIS WORLD, AND NOW I HAVE MADE THE WORLD PART OF ME.

NO, BUT I'D SURE LIKE TO SIT NEXT TO YOU IN A *GEOGRAPHY EXAM.*

I BELIEVE IN A PLANET *FREE* OF EXPLOITATION AND POLLUTION BY WEALTHY CORPORATIONS AND MULTINATIONALS, WHO WOULD DESTROY EVERYTHING FOR *GREED.*

THAT TIME IS FAST APPROACHING, BUT STILL THE FAT CATS LINE THEIR POCKETS. *YOUR FATHER* IS SUCH A MAN.

NO, SEE, YOU'VE GOT IT ALL WRONG—

LIAR! YOUR FATHER'S FORTUNE IS BUILT ON STOLEN *OIL!* HIS PIPELINES HAVE *SCARRED* THREE CONTINENTS!

SO EITHER MY APPENDIX HAS **MOVED**, OR THAT HOSPITAL HAS **REALLY** STUPID DOCTORS.

YOU CAN CUT OFF ALL THE FINGERS YOU WANT, BUT NIKOLEI DREVIN WON'T PAY A **PENNY** FOR THEM. HE DOESN'T EVEN KNOW I EXIST.

NOW, CAN I GO?

I THINK NOT. IF YOU ARE REALLY **NOT** PAUL DREVIN, THEN NOBODY CARES ABOUT YOU. WE CAN KILL YOU **ANYWAY**.

SO PERHAPS, **ALEX RIDER**, IT WOULD HAVE BEEN BETTER FOR YOU IF THERE HAD BEEN NO MISTAKE. LOSING **ONE FINGER** MIGHT HAVE BEEN EASIER.

TAKE HIM BACK TO THE ROOM. I WILL MAKE ENQUIRIES ... AND THEN **DEAL** WITH HIM.

MMF! THAT'S IT...

...JUST HOPE MY **CHEST STITCHES** HOLD!

NNNH!

HOPEFULLY THAT'S THE **HARDEST** PART DONE. BUT I'M NOT SAFE **YET!**

HANDRAIL'S **BOILING** HOT — THE FIRE MUST BE **CLOSE!**

GROUND FLOOR... WHERE'S THE *EXIT*...

SOMEONE'S THERE... WHO...?

CLEVER BOY, AIN'T YA? BUT NOT FOR LONG!

IT'S THE ONE IN THE *COMBAT JACKET*! HE STAYED *BEHIND*, TO MAKE SURE!

THAT SEALS IT — THE ONLY WAY OUT IS *UP*!

NNH! NO TIME... AND NO WAY DOWN...

...BUT MAYBE THERE'S A WAY *ACROSS*!

I'LL NEVER *CRAWL* ACROSS THAT BANNER. BUT *UNCLE IAN* ONCE TOLD ME THAT TIGHTROPE WALKING IS ALL ABOUT *LOWERING* YOUR CENTRE OF GRAVITY...

HORNCHURCH TOWERS

...AND THIS *RUBBISH* THE BUILDERS LEFT BEHIND WILL DO EXACTLY THAT!

...AND THEN THE FIREMEN TOOK ME BACK TO HOSPITAL, AND PAUL DREVIN WAS GONE.

THAT'S ALL I CAN TELL YOU, *MR CRAWFORD.*

MMM. AND THE DOCTOR INSISTED YOU *REST* FOR TWO WEEKS, YES?

THEY WON'T EVEN LET ME GO BACK TO *SCHOOL.*

AND HE KEEPS MASSAGING HIS LEFT ARM.

HIS LEFT...?

AH, YES. I SEE.

YEAH, YOU KNOW. WHERE HE WAS *SHOT,* OUTSIDE YOUR OFFICE!

I HAD A RUN-IN WITH SCORPIA *MYSELF* ABOUT TEN YEARS AGO, AND IT NEARLY DID FOR ME. BUT I KNEW *YOU'D* BE STRONG ENOUGH TO PULL THROUGH.

I WORKED WITH YOUR *FATHER* A COUPLE OF TIMES, YOU KNOW. I WASN'T ALLOWED TO TELL YOU BEFORE.

YOU WORKED WITH HIM? IN THE FIELD?

YES. THAT WAS BEFORE... WELL, I GOT *HURT* AND HAD TO MOVE BACK BEHIND A DESK. BUT I SEE A LOT OF HIM IN YOU, ALEX. IT'S REMARKABLE.

NOW, FOR YOUR OWN SAFETY, I'LL FILL YOU IN.

PAUL'S FATHER IS *NIKOLEI DREVIN*, THE RUSSIAN MULTIBILLIONAIRE. WONDERFUL MAN – HE LIVES IN ENGLAND MOST OF THE TIME NOW.

THEY *SAID* IT WAS DREVIN THEY WERE AFTER. DIDN'T HE BUY *STRATFORD EAST* FOOTBALL CLUB, AND SPEND A FORTUNE ON THEM?

HE CAN AFFORD IT. HE HAS HOUSES ALL OVER THE WORLD, AND EVEN OWNS A CARIBBEAN ISLAND, *FLAMINGO BAY*. THAT'S WHERE THE LAUNCHES FOR *ARK ANGEL* TAKE PLACE.

ARK ANGEL IS A *SPACE HOTEL* THAT DREVIN'S BUILDING. IT GOES TOGETHER PIECE BY PIECE, SO HE SENDS *ROCKETS* UP CARRYING PARTS.

THE *BRITISH GOVERNMENT* ARE PARTNERS ON THE PROJECT. WE'RE ALL VERY EXCITED. THE FIRST HOTEL IN SPACE WILL FLY A *BRITISH* FLAG!

UH... I'LL ASK HIM.

I DON'T BELIEVE IT! **NIKOLEI DREVIN'S** ON THE PHONE! HE WANTS US TO HAVE TEA WITH HIM THIS AFTERNOON AT THE **WATERFRONT HOTEL!**

DO YOU THINK WE SHOULD? I MEAN, THE **LAST** TIME I MET A MULTIMILLIONAIRE WAS **DAMIAN CRAY**. THAT DIDN'T END WELL...

MILLION, SHMILLION. DREVIN'S A MULTI**BILLION**AIRE! AND YOU SAVED HIM A LOT OF MONEY. HE MIGHT BE **VERY** GRATEFUL...

OK, TELL HIM WE'LL BE THERE. LET'S HAVE SOME FUN.

YAY!

HAHA! PLUS, I SUPPOSE THIS TIME THE ENEMY IS KASPAR, NOT **DREVIN**...

I DON'T THINK A **GRAND ENTRANCE** WOULD HAVE BEEN WISE, JACK.

WHEN HE SAID HE WAS SENDING A CAR, I EXPECTED A **LIMO,** NOT A BLACK CAB.

YOU MUST BE **ALEX** AND **JACK,** RIGHT? MR DREVIN ASKED ME TO COME GET YOU.

I'M **TAMARA KNIGHT,** HIS PERSONAL ASSISTANT.

AHEM

SO, ANYWAY...

A FELLOW **YANK,** HUH? CAREFUL, ALEX, YOU'RE SURROUNDED BY **FOREIGNERS!**

MR DREVIN IS IN A **PRESS CONFERENCE.** YOU'RE WELCOME TO LOOK IN IF YOU WANT, OR YOU CAN WAIT IN HIS **PRIVATE SUITE.**

HE OWNS THE HOTEL, YOU SEE.

...AND SO, *ARK ANGEL* REALLY WILL MAKE SPACE TOURISM FOR THE MASSES A *REALITY*. THANK YOU.

CLAPCLAPCLAPCLAPCLAP

MR DREVIN, ARK ANGEL IS *ALREADY* TWO MONTHS BEHIND SCHEDULE AND *THREE HUNDRED MILLION DOLLARS* OVER BUDGET. DO YOU REGRET GETTING INVOLVED?

THIS IS THE MOST *AMBITIOUS* BUILDING PROJECT IN HISTORY. A FUNCTIONING HOTEL IN SPACE! OF *COURSE* I DON'T REGRET IT.

A HUNDRED YEARS FROM NOW, IT WILL BE *COMMONPLACE* TO TRAVEL TO THE EDGE OF THE UNIVERSE. AND IT ALL BEGINS *HERE*, WITH ARK ANGEL.

DREVIN'S SMALLER AND PLAINER THAN I *IMAGINED*. BUT HE HANDLES JOURNALISTS WELL.

DOES IT *BOTHER* YOU THAT THE PEOPLE WHO TRIED TO KIDNAP YOUR SON ARE STILL AT LARGE?

THAT WILL BE ALL, MISS KNIGHT. YOU HAVE MADE THE ARRANGEMENTS FOR *SATURDAY*?

YES, MR DREVIN. THE FILE IS ON YOUR DESK.

I AM *VERY* HAPPY TO MEET YOU, ALEX RIDER. I OWE YOU *SO* MUCH.

HOW'S *PAUL*? IS HE RECOVERING WELL FROM HIS OPERATION?

HE IS, THANK YOU. AND THANKS TO YOU. WHAT YOU DID WAS *INCREDIBLE.*

YOU MUST KNOW HOW WEALTHY I AM, ALEX. IF THERE IS *ANYTHING* IN THE WORLD YOU DESIRE, I CAN GIVE IT TO YOU.

THAT'S OK. I'M GLAD I WAS ABLE TO *HELP*, BUT IT JUST SORT OF HAPPENED. I DON'T NEED A REWARD.

SO **MODEST**! BUT I THOUGHT YOU MIGHT SAY THAT, SO I HAVE DONATED **TWO MILLION POUNDS** TO ST DOMINIC'S ON YOUR BEHALF.

AND NOW I WOULD LIKE YOU TO **STAY** WITH ME, AS A **GUEST**, WHILE YOU RECUPERATE.

I AM CERTAIN **PAUL** WOULD ENJOY YOUR COMPANY.

PAUL? BUT WE HARDLY **KNOW** EACH OTHER.

BECAUSE OF MY WORK, PAUL DOESN'T MEET MANY BOYS HIS OWN AGE. AND THERE IS ALWAYS A DANGER SOMEONE WILL **USE** HIM TO GET TO ME, LIKE AT THE HOSPITAL.

PLEASE, ALEX. TWO WEEKS OF LUXURY! THIS WEEKEND WE WILL WATCH MY **FOOTBALL TEAM** PLAY CHELSEA. NEXT WEEK, WE WILL SEE A **ROCKET LAUNCH** AT FLAMINGO BAY.

WHAT DO YOU SAY?

ALL RIGHT, THEN. BUT I SHOULD WARN YOU...

...I'M A **CHELSEA** SUPPORTER.

WHAT YOU DID WAS *AMAZING*, ALEX. THOSE MEN NEARLY KILLED YOU BECAUSE OF *ME*! I'M GLAD YOU AGREED TO COME.

YOUR FATHER MADE IT *HARD* TO REFUSE.

YEAH, HE'S LIKE THAT.

HHHHH

SORRY, JUST A MINUTE. I HAVE *ASTHMA*.

HHHHH

WE'VE GOT *THIRTY* BEDROOMS AND THEY'RE NEVER FULL, SO THIS IS YOURS.

YOU'VE GOT A 100-INCH PLASMA TV, BLU-RAY, ALL THE LATEST CONSOLES, A *BUTLER* ON SPEED DIAL... ANYTHING YOU WANT, JUST PICK UP THE PHONE.

I'M SORRY, THIS MUST BE WEIRD. YOU DON'T EVEN KNOW ME, YOU PROBABLY THINK I'M A *SPOILT BRAT*...

BUT MONEY CAN'T BUY FRIENDS. I'LL UNDERSTAND IF YOU WANT TO TURN AROUND AND GO. SOMETIMES *I* FEEL LIKE THAT.

NO... I CAN'T GO BACK TO SCHOOL AND I'M MEANT TO BE RESTING, SO WHY *NOT* LET YOUR DAD TREAT ME LIKE A MILLIONAIRE FOR A WHILE?

COOL! THEN I'LL SEE YOU AT DINNER.

LATER:

...WE'LL WATCH THE *FOOTBALL* TOMORROW, GO TO *NEW YORK* ON SUNDAY, AND THEN HEAD DOWN TO *FLAMINGO BAY.* HAVE YOU EVER BEEN *KITE-SURFING?*

ER ... NO.

I'LL SHOW YOU. WE'RE ON THE ATLANTIC SIDE, SO WE GET *GREAT* WAVES.

AND HOW IS YOUR *INJURY,* ALEX? REMIND ME WHAT HAPPENED TO YOU?

I WENT OVER MY *BIKE'S* HANDLEBARS AND HIT A FENCE.

TO RECEIVE SUCH AN INJURY FALLING OFF A *BICYCLE,* YOU MUST HAVE BEEN GOING *VERY* FAST.

I WAS, *UNTIL* I HIT THE FENCE.

WHAT *USED* TO BE HERE, BEFORE YOU BUILT THIS CASTLE?

SOME *GHASTLY* OLD MANOR HOUSE. SADLY, IT BURNED DOWN.

A *TERRIBLE* ACCIDENT.

SO, I AM TOLD THAT GIRL *JACK* IS NOT YOUR MOTHER?

MY PARENTS *DIED* WHEN I WAS VERY YOUNG, IN A PLANE CRASH.

ANOTHER TERRIBLE ACCIDENT.

AND NOW MISS STARBRIGHT LOOKS AFTER YOU? IT IS VERY *UNUSUAL*. BUT THEN, IT SEEMS TO ME YOU ARE A VERY *UNUSUAL* BOY.

IT WOULD BE INTERESTING, I THINK, TO HAVE A *SON* LIKE YOU.

KOF!

KOF!

HHHNNNNN!

FOR GOD'S SAKE, PAUL, USE YOUR *INHALER!*

LEFT FRONT POCKET, PAUL.

HHHHH

THANKS, ALEX.

UH... SORRY, I WAS JUST ON MY WAY TO *BED*, AND WONDERED WHAT WAS IN HERE...

...YOU'VE MET THE *QUEEN!*

SEVERAL TIMES, ACTUALLY. SHE *NEVER* STOPS TALKING ABOUT HER HORSES. QUITE BORING.

BUT THIS IS MY *PRIVATE STUDY.* YOU SHOULD NOT BE HERE.

YOU'RE... YOU'RE RIGHT, I'M SORRY.

GOODNIGHT, MR DREVIN.

I DON'T GET IT. THIS FILE IS FOR A *FOURTEEN-YEAR-OLD KID*. WHAT'S IT GOT TO DO WITH *US*?

ALEX RIDER IS AN *AGENT* WORKING WITH *MI6 SPECIAL OPS*.

WHAT?!

IS BLUNT *CRAZY*?

THAT'S *IMPOSSIBLE*!

HARD TO BELIEVE, I *KNOW*. BUT ALEX RIDER IS THE NEAREST THING MI6 HAS TO A *LETHAL WEAPON*.

I DON'T KNOW HOW HE GOT MIXED UP WITH DREVIN. MAYBE IT WAS COINCIDENCE... MAYBE IT *WASN'T*.

ALEX RID

BUT ONE WAY OR ANOTHER, HE'S GOING TO HELP *US*.

BRING HIM TO ME, AND I'LL MAKE SURE OF THAT.

HAVE YOU **ALWAYS** SUPPORTED CHELSEA, ALEX?

YES. I LIVE JUST DOWN THE ROAD FROM HERE.

I **MET** ROMAN ABRAMOVICH A FEW TIMES, IN MOSCOW. WE DID NOT GET ALONG.

SO I HOPE TO DISAPPOINT **BOTH** OF YOU TODAY! **HA!**

STAMFORD BRIDGE, CHELSEA

IT IS PROBABLY FOR THE BEST THAT PAUL'S ASTHMA KEPT HIM AT HOME TODAY. TOO MANY **PEOPLE** AROUND.

DO YOU REALLY THINK HE'S STILL IN **DANGER**?

HE IS **MY** SON.

GOOD AFTERNOON, MR DREVIN. I'VE GOT **ALL-ACCESS PASSES** FOR BOTH YOU AND ALEX. LUNCH IS ON THE THIRD FLOOR.

LATER:

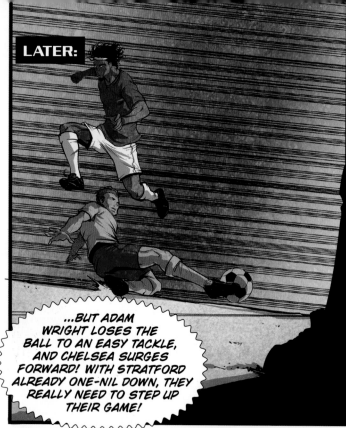

...BUT ADAM WRIGHT LOSES THE BALL TO AN EASY TACKLE, AND CHELSEA SURGES FORWARD! WITH STRATFORD ALREADY ONE-NIL DOWN, THEY REALLY NEED TO STEP UP THEIR GAME!

AND THERE IT IS, A POWERHOUSE IN THE BACK OF THE NET! TWO-NIL TO CHELSEA, AND NOW SURELY THE QUESTIONS AROUND WRIGHT'S LEADERSHIP MUST BE STRONGER THAN EVER!

WHAT THE HELL IS WRIGHT *DOING*? I PAID *MILLIONS* FOR THAT PRETTY BOY, AND HE'S BARELY *TOUCHED* THE BALL ALL GAME!

ARE YOU *ENJOYING* YOUR STAY WITH MR DREVIN?

IT'S FINE. ARE YOU A FOOTBALL FAN?

I HOPE MR DREVIN'S TEAM *WINS*, OF COURSE, BUT I DON'T REALLY CARE. I ONLY GOT THIS JOB THROUGH AN *AGENCY*.

TAMARA KNIGHT... I CAN'T WORK HER OUT. SHE'S MEGA-EFFICIENT, BUT DOESN'T ACTUALLY SEEM INTERESTED IN *ANYTHING*. WEIRD.

TWO...

...ONE.
WHAT A
SCORE!

I CAN'T **SPEAK**, BUT THAT AND A **MIDDLE FINGER** MIGHT BE ENOUGH TO GET HIM ANGRY...

YOU GOT A **PROBLEM**, SUNSHINE? LOOKING FOR **TROUBLE**?

WHAT ARE YOU **TALKING** ABOUT? GET OUT OF THE WAY, YOU **MORON**!

TIME TO MOVE!

FORCE THREE ARE HERE! THEY GAVE WRIGHT A WEIRD MEDALLION IN THE CHANGING ROOMS. IT'S MADE OF "CAESIUM"?

WHAT?!

THIS IS TAMARA KNIGHT! GET SECURITY TO THE CHANGING ROOMS!

DO NOT LET ADAM WRIGHT INTO THE SHOWER!

CAESIUM IS INCREDIBLY VOLATILE IN WATER. IF HE WEARS THAT MEDALLION IN THE SHOWER...

MISS KNIGHT? THIS IS THE POLICE. WE'RE ALREADY IN THE CHANGING ROOMS...

...LOOKS LIKE THERE'S BEEN SOME KIND OF FREAK EXPLOSION.

I'M AFRAID ADAM WRIGHT'S TAKEN HIS LAST PENALTY.

YOU STILL WON'T *BEAT* ME, ALEX...

...EVEN *THIRTY-SIX THOUSAND FEET* IN THE AIR!

NIKOLEI DREVIN'S PRIVATE 747, SOMEWHERE OVER THE ATLANTIC

THIS PLANE IS *AMAZING*, PAUL. IF IT WASN'T FOR THE NOISE OF THE ENGINES, I MIGHT *FORGET* WE WERE FLYING AT ALL!

YEAH, MY FATHER KNOWS HOW TO SPEND HIS *MONEY*. COME ON, LET'S WATCH A FILM.

LET ME GET A *DRINK* FIRST.

GOOD *BOOK*, MS KNIGHT?

SURE.

LADIES AND GENTS, WE'RE JUST COMING IN TO *LAND*. PLEASE REMAIN *SEATED* AND RELAX WHILE WE WAIT FOR *CUSTOMS AND IMMIGRATION*.

I GUESS SOMEONE LIKE YOUR DAD DOESN'T NEED TO *QUEUE UP* LIKE EVERYONE ELSE.

DEFINITELY NOT. *THEY* COME TO *US*.

WELCOME TO NEW YORK, MR DREVIN. *PASSPORTS*, EVERYONE, PLEASE.

ALL RIGHT, LET'S JUST *SCAN* THIS BABY THROUGH HERE...

...*THERE* WE GO. THANK YOU, SIR.

BEEEP!

CIA LOCAL STATION, NEW YORK

ALEX! SO GOOD TO SEE YOU AGAIN!

JOE BYRNE!

I SHOULD HAVE **KNOWN** SOMETHING WAS UP! SHULSKY **SWITCHED** MY PASSPORT FOR A FAKE WHEN HE WAS **SCANNING** IT, DIDN'T HE?

SORRY ABOUT THAT. BUT YOU AND I NEED TO HAVE A LITTLE CHAT, **FAR** AWAY FROM ANYWHERE **NIKOLEI DREVIN** CAN LISTEN IN.

I NEVER DID THANK YOU FOR THE WORK YOU DID ON **SKELETON KEY**.

I WAS SORRY ABOUT YOUR **AGENTS**, TOM AND BELINDA.

SO WAS I. BUT THAT WASN'T YOUR FAULT. YOU DID A **GREAT** JOB.

AND NOW I'M HOPING YOU CAN HELP US AGAIN.

SORRY, BUT I ALREADY DECIDED THAT I DON'T WANT *ANY* MORE TO DO WITH DREVIN. JUST PUT ME ON A PLANE TO WASHINGTON, AND I'LL SAY *GOODBYE*.

FUNNY YOU SHOULD MENTION *WASHINGTON*. ANYWAY, YOU CAN'T JUST WALK OUT OF HERE. YOU'RE AN *ILLEGAL IMMIGRANT*, REMEMBER?

JUST HEAR ME OUT. YOU HAVE *NO IDEA* HOW MUCH IS AT STAKE.

IF I HAD A *PENNY* FOR EVERY TIME I'VE HEARD THAT... ALL RIGHT, GO ON. WHAT IS IT *THIS* TIME?

THE FACT IS, YOU'RE IN A *UNIQUE* SITUATION RIGHT NOW. AND AS YOU'VE PROBABLY GUESSED, THIS IS *ALL* ABOUT *DREVIN*.

NIKOLEI VLADIMIR **DREVIN**. BY OUR COUNT, HE'S THE FIFTH RICHEST MAN ALIVE. YOU BRITISH JUST **LOVE** HIM.

AND NOW WITH **ARK ANGEL** HE'S GOING TO HELP THE BRITISH CORNER THE MARKET IN **SPACE TOURISM**.

BUT YOU'RE **INVESTIGATING** HIM, AREN'T YOU? THAT'S **WHY** YOU DRAGGED ME IN HERE.

WE'RE TALKING **ORGANIZED CRIME**, ALEX. ALL ROADS LEAD TO DREVIN.

DESPITE HIS FRIENDS IN HIGH PLACES, WE THINK HE'S THE WORLD'S **BIGGEST CRIMINAL**.

IT GOES BACK TO THE COLLAPSE OF THE **SOVIET UNION** IN THE NINETIES. THEIR GOVERNMENT WAS BROKE. TO RAISE MONEY, THEY **SOLD OFF** THEIR INDUSTRIES TO CORRUPT BUSINESSMEN FOR MERE PENNIES.

IT'S **HARD** TO GET REAL INFO OUT OF RUSSIA FROM THAT TIME PERIOD, BUT WE DO KNOW DREVIN WAS A SENIOR **KGB** MAN. AND WHEN THE SELL-OFF HAPPENED, HE **DIDN'T** HAVE ENOUGH MONEY.

AND HE **USED** THOSE MILLIONS TO BUY UP THE INDUSTRIES AND MAKE HIS **FORTUNE**, RIGHT?

RIGHT. BUT **LEGITIMATE** IT WAS NOT. HE JUST ABOUT STOLE THE RUSSIAN PEOPLE'S **OWN OIL** FROM THEM.

WHAT HE **DID** HAVE, THANKS TO HIS KGB WORK, WAS CRIMINAL CONTACTS. THE RUSSIAN **MAFIYA**. THE JAPANESE **YAKUZA**. THE CHINESE **TRIADS**. THEY ALL LENT HIM **MILLIONS**.

SURE, THERE WERE **PROTESTS** AND A **POLICE INQUIRY**... BUT PEOPLE WHO SPOKE UP WERE **MURDERED**. ANYONE WHO EVEN SNEEZED AT DREVIN WAS AS GOOD AS DEAD.

SO PEOPLE WENT **QUIET**, AND DREVIN MADE A LOT OF MONEY. BUT PEOPLE LIKE THAT ALWAYS WANT **MORE**. IT'S NEVER ENOUGH.

HE BECAME A **BANKER** FOR THOSE CRIMINAL ORGANIZATIONS. THAT'S WHERE THE REAL MONEY STARTED ROLLING IN.

ARMS SALES TO TERRORISTS. **DRUG TRAFFICKING**. **PROSTITUTION** RACKETS. WE ESTIMATE DREVIN'S CASH FLOW IS BEHIND JUST ABOUT **EVERY** DIRTY DEAL DONE AROUND THE WORLD RIGHT NOW.

GREAT! AND DON'T WORRY ABOUT PAUL. HE'LL BE FINE. I EXPECT HE'LL GO BACK TO HIS **MOTHER.**

NOW, THERE'S SOMEONE HERE WE'RE **SURE** YOU'LL WANT TO SEE...

SMITHERS!

ALEX, DEAR BOY! YOU LOOK TREMENDOUSLY WELL. MRS JONES SENDS HER BEST WISHES.

SHE **KNOWS** I'M HERE?

OH, YES, WE'VE BEEN KEEPING AN **EYE** ON YOU. AND I THOUGHT YOU MIGHT LIKE A **GADGET** OR TWO, IN CASE YOU RUN INTO TROUBLE.

I WAS TOLD THERE WOULDN'T **BE** ANY TROUBLE.

YES, WELL...

AHEM

ANYWAY, FIRST OFF...

ANYWAY, ONE LAST THING. FLAMINGO BAY IS A *TROPICAL* ISLAND, SO THIS MIGHT HELP...

YOU CAN ALSO USE IT TO CONTACT THE *CIA*. TAP THE POWER BUTTON TEN TIMES AND SPEAK INTO IT.

I'VE GOT A VERSION FULL OF *PLASTIC EXPLOSIVE*, BUT MR BLUNT WON'T LET ME GIVE IT TO YOU. I CALL IT THE *I-X-PLOD!*

IT'S NOT *REALLY* MOSQUITO REPELLENT, OF COURSE. IN FACT, IT DOES THE OPPOSITE – IT *ATTRACTS* MOSQUITOES ... AND JUST ABOUT EVERY OTHER INSECT ON THE ISLAND!

COULD BE USEFUL FOR A DIVERSION.

NOW, I'M OFF TO TEST MY *SHARK-REPELLENT SWIMMING TRUNKS* IN ST LUCIA, SO I WON'T BE TOO FAR AWAY IF YOU NEED ME.

PIP-PIP!

YOU KNOW, I'M ALMOST BEGINNING TO THINK BLUNT PUT ME IN THAT ROOM NEXT TO PAUL *DELIBERATELY...*

OH, I COULDN'T *POSSIBLY* COMMENT ON THAT.

WE CONTROL *EVERYTHING* FROM HERE. MOST OF IT'S *COMPUTERIZED*, BUT WITH FOUR TONNES OF EQUIPMENT FLYING THROUGH SPACE, WE CAN'T AFFORD *MISTAKES!*

THERE WILL BE *NO MISTAKES*. WE LAUNCH WEDNESDAY AT *0900*, ON SCHEDULE.

CAN WE GET CLOSER THAN THIS WHEN IT LAUNCHES?

ANY CLOSER AND YOU'D BE *DEAFENED*. THE VIBRATIONS FROM GABRIEL 7'S LAUNCH WOULD *DESTROY* YOUR EARDRUMS. EVEN IN HERE WE'LL NEED TO BE COMPLETELY INSULATED.

MR DREVIN, I MUST ASK FOR A MOMENT OF YOUR TIME, TO DISCUSS *LAUNCH TRAJECTORY* DISPERSIONS.

OF COURSE, PROFESSOR. MAGNUS, PLEASE SHOW THE BOYS OUT.

DREVIN ISN'T ACTING LIKE HE'S ABOUT TO RUN AWAY... I HAVE A TERRIBLE FEELING HE'S UP TO *SOMETHING*. BUT WHAT?

THE ROCKET LAUNCHES IN FORTY-FIVE HOURS... I *HAVE* TO FIND OUT BEFORE THEN!

TIME TO TRY OUT SMITHERS' *IPOD!*

...FINAL PREPARATIONS. I WANT *ALL* THE PROGRAMMING DOUBLE-CHECKED... YES, THE BOAT COMES IN AT *ELEVEN PM*, BEHIND THE LAUNCH SITE. I'LL BE *WAITING...*

WHAT ARE YOU *DOING*, ALEX? ARE YOU TAKING *THAT* WITH YOU?

NO, I WAS ... JUST CHECKING IT'S *WORKING*.

ARE YOU SURE YOU'RE *OK* WITH ME GOING DIVING?

I'LL BE FINE. I'VE GOT *USED* TO BEING ON MY OWN.

YOU CERTAINLY DON'T LOOK LIKE A *SECRETARY* ANY MORE. I DON'T UNDERSTAND...

JOE BYRNE TOLD YOU HE HAD SOMEONE ON THE ISLAND. BUT I *COULDN'T* ACKNOWLEDGE YOU. IT WOULD HAVE BLOWN MY COVER.

AND YOU *TOLD* ME YOU WERE GOING TO DIVE, REMEMBER? I FIGURED SOMETHING MIGHT BE UP.

I THINK DREVIN IS *LEAVING* TONIGHT.

BUT THE GABRIEL 7 *LAUNCHES* TOMORROW, AND THAT MEANS *EVERYTHING* TO HIM.

I KNOW, BUT I OVERHEARD A *CALL*. THERE'S A *BOAT* ARRIVING AT ELEVEN TONIGHT.

THEN WE'LL *BE* THERE. IF DREVIN TRIES TO LEAVE, WE CAN ALERT THE CIA IN *BARBADOS* AND THEY'LL BE HERE IN *TEN MINUTES*.

MEANWHILE, I'LL SNEAK YOU SOME *CLOTHES* FROM THE HOUSE. CAN I GET YOU ANYTHING ELSE?

YOU ALREADY SAVED MY *LIFE*, TAMARA.

BUT I'D LOVE A SANDWICH. I'M *STARVING*.

PERFECT TIMING. HERE'S THE RELIEF NIGHT WATCH NOW...

PSHHH!

...AND ONE OF THEM IS *KOLO!* GOOD. IF ANYONE *DESERVES* TO SUFFER, IT'S HIM.

BUT SHE SEEMS TO ACTUALLY *ENJOY* THE DANGER AND ADVENTURE. I GUESS THAT'S THE *REAL* DIFFERENCE BETWEEN US.

ARE YOU *SURE* THAT STINGO SPRAY WILL WORK?

DON'T WORRY, TAMARA.

SMITHERS HAS NEVER LET ME DOWN YET...

NO, HE WAS IN THE HOSPITAL BECAUSE HE'D BEEN *SHOT*. I'VE SEEN THEIR RECORDS.

THEN PERHAPS IT *IS* AN UNHAPPY COINCIDENCE. UNHAPPY FOR *YOU*, THAT IS.

BUT FOR ME, IT IS AN *OPPORTUNITY*. YOU SEE, I'D LIKE TO EXPLAIN TO PAUL, BUT HE'S TOO *WEAK*. HE MIGHT EVEN *HATE* ME FOR WHAT I'M ABOUT TO TELL YOU.

BUT YOU, I KNOW, WILL *UNDERSTAND*.

I AM ONE OF THE RICHEST MEN ON THE PLANET, YES. EVEN MY MANY *ACCOUNTANTS* AREN'T QUITE SURE HOW MUCH I'M WORTH.

CAN YOU IMAGINE BEING ABLE TO HAVE *ANYTHING* YOU WANT? ENTERING A SHOP TO BUY A SUIT, AND INSTEAD BUYING THE *SHOP*? SEEING A NEW AEROPLANE, AND *BUYING* IT BEFORE THE DAY IS OUT?

OF COURSE YOU CAN'T.

NO DOUBT YOU KNOW THIS WEALTH WAS **NOT** ACCUMULATED IN WAYS YOU WOULD CALL **"HONEST"**. SUCH TERMS MEAN NOTHING TO ME.

I AM A CRIMINAL. I **ADMIT** IT. I HAVE KILLED AND ORDERED PEOPLE TO BE KILLED. THIS DOES **NOT** TROUBLE ME.

WHY SHOULD IT? **EVERY** SUCCESSFUL BUSINESSMAN HAS LIED AND CHEATED AT SOME TIME. IT'S JUST A QUESTION OF **DEGREE**.

BUT EIGHTEEN MONTHS AGO, TWO **PROBLEMS** CAME TO MY ATTENTION, AND THEY HAVE **FORCED** ME INTO A PARTICULAR COURSE OF ACTION.

THEY ARE WHY YOU ARE HERE, ALEX RIDER.

"THE FIRST PROBLEM CONCERNS THE **STATE DEPARTMENT OF THE USA** INVESTIGATING MY FINANCIAL DEALINGS."

OF COURSE, I HAVE ALWAYS **KNOWN** THEY WERE BUILDING A CASE AGAINST ME.

BUT I AM A CAREFUL MAN. I DO **NOT** LEAVE PAPER EVIDENCE, OR WITNESSES.

SHOW HIM, MAGNUS.

WHAT THE...?

KASPAR!

I *KNEW* I'D SEEN "PAYNE" SOMEWHERE BEFORE...

A RISK WE HAD TO TAKE. THE *TATTOOS* WERE RATHER PAINFUL, OF COURSE. BUT I THINK WE SUCCEEDED IN CREATING A TERRORIST PEOPLE WOULD *REMEMBER*, DON'T YOU?

I WOULD HAVE LIKED TO GET TO KNOW YOU *BETTER*, ALEX. BUT I DO NOT THINK OUR *ORBITS* WILL EVER CROSS AGAIN.

TAKE HIM AWAY.

IN THERE.

OOOOOO! EEEEEEEEE!

MEET *ARTHUR*, YOUR FELLOW PRISONER.

ANY RELATION?

YOU ALREADY KNOW *MS KNIGHT*, OF COURSE.

YOU'LL *HEAR* THE ROCKET LAUNCH. WHEN IT'S GONE, SOMEONE WILL TAKE YOU TO THE BEACH, AND THAT WILL BE YOUR *END*.

I'M JUST SORRY I WON'T BE THERE TO SEE IT. BUT I'LL BE *THINKING* OF YOU.

...AND THAT'S DREVIN'S ENTIRE, *INSANE* PLAN. I CAN HARDLY BELIEVE IT, BUT HE DIDN'T *SEEM* TO BE LYING.

WE HAVE TO CONTACT JOE BYRNE SOMEHOW, AND *FAST!*

WHY NOT BOTH OF US?

ALL THIS TIME, WE THOUGHT HE WAS FINISHED AND LOOKING FOR AN *ESCAPE*...

THE GUARDS TOOK MY *TRANSMITTER*, AND PROBABLY YOUR *IPOD*. SO EITHER WE STOP HIM OURSELVES, OR *YOU'LL* HAVE TO GET HELP.

UH, *BULLET* IN MY SHOULDER, REMEMBER?

BUT YOU'RE NOT THE ONLY ONE WITH *GADGETS.*

DIAMOND-EDGED TUNGSTEN WIRE IN MY LACES. IT'LL CUT THROUGH THE BARS, GIVEN ENOUGH TIME.

AND BEFORE YOU ASK, THE GUARDS ALREADY TOOK MY *EXPLODING EARRINGS.*

THEN I'D BETTER GET TO WORK. I'LL START BY FREEING MY *WRISTS*...

LATER:

GOT IT!

NO, ALEX. THERE'S NO TIME!

GET TO *BARBADOS.* FIND ED SHULSKY. I'LL SURVIVE TILL YOU GET BACK.

HANG ON, TAMARA. I'LL GET *YOU* OUT, TOO.

HANG IN THERE. I'LL COME BACK FOR YOU, I *PROMISE.*

BUT *FIRST,* I NEED TO GET OFF THE ISLAND SOMEHOW...

...AND THIS *DISGUISE* MIGHT JUST DO THE TRICK!

EVERYONE *THINKS* TAMARA AND I ARE STILL LOCKED UP. IT'S NO SURPRISE SECURITY'S *RELAXED.*

DAMMIT, NO *KEY* FOR THE BOAT. NOT *THAT* RELAXED, THEN.

ONLY *ONE* THING FOR IT. I HOPED IT WOULDN'T COME TO THIS... *TEN MILES* ON A *KITE BOARD* WON'T BE EASY, EVEN WITH THE WIND IN MY FAVOUR.

ALEX?

I... I THOUGHT YOU'D *GONE*. WHAT HAPPENED?

AND WHY ON EARTH ARE YOU *DRESSED* LIKE THAT?

I CAN'T TELL YOU, PAUL. I'M SORRY.

DO YOU KNOW WHERE THE KEY TO THE BOAT IS?

DAD TOLD ME YOU'D BEEN SENT HERE TO *SPY* ON HIM. *I* SAID THAT COULDN'T BE TRUE, BUT HE SAID HIS ENEMIES IN NEW YORK *PAID* YOU TO COME HERE AND MAKE TROUBLE.

DID HE TELL YOU WHAT HE DID TO ME?!

OH, NEVER MIND. LOOK, JUST—

NO!

THIS IS AN *ALARM*, ALEX. IF I PRESS IT, A *DOZEN GUARDS* WILL BE HERE IN LESS THAN A MINUTE. NOW TELL ME THE *TRUTH*.

AND NOW THE BOAT'S *OUT OF CONTROL...*

IT'S COMING STRAIGHT FOR US! *ABANDON SHIP!*

BOOM!

TWO DOWN... BUT THE *YACHT* IS STILL COMING!

AND THEY *WON'T* MAKE THE SAME MISTAKES. THEY'LL CUT ME DOWN AS SOON AS THEY'RE IN *RANGE!*

OF COURSE NOT. NO, ALL WE HAVE TO DO IS FIND THE *RED BUTTON!*

THE WHAT?

THE *SELF-DESTRUCT!* THERE MUST BE A FALLBACK, IN CASE SOMETHING WENT *WRONG* WITH THE LAUNCH. WE'LL BE ABLE TO BLOW THE ROCKET UP *BEFORE* IT REACHES ARK ANGEL.

BUT WE'VE GOT TO MOVE *FAST.* AND THAT'S WHY YOU HAVE TO COME WITH US. THERE'S JUST NO *TIME* TO TAKE YOU BACK TO LAND.

THAT'S... THAT'S OK.

I PROMISED *TAMARA* I'D GET HER OUT... AND I'D LIKE TO *EXPLAIN* PROPERLY TO PAUL.

THIRTY SECONDS!

ALEX, I WANT YOU TO STAY **ON BOARD** UNTIL THE FIGHTING'S OVER.

WHAT? BUT—

THIS IS GOING TO BE A **WAR**. I CAN'T AFFORD TO HAVE MY MEN **WORRYING** ABOUT YOU.

HANG ON... THAT **CESSNA PLANE** WASN'T THERE WHEN I TOOK THE KITE BOARD. IS DREVIN ALREADY PLANNING HIS **ESCAPE**?

THE AMERICANS HAVE TAKEN ALL THE **WEAPONS**, BUT I NEED TO **DISABLE** THAT SEAPLANE SOMEHOW.

BRAKKA! BRAKKA!

MACHINE-GUN FIRE. SO THE *FIGHTING'S* STARTED.

BOOM!

BRAKKA! BRAKKA!

BRAKKA! BRAKKA!

BRAKKA! BRAKKA!

AND THERE'S *DREVIN!* HE'S DRIVING STRAIGHT FOR THE CESSNA...

...WAIT, NO, HE'S GONE *PAST* IT! HE MUST NEED SOMETHING FROM THE HOUSE BEFORE HE LEAVES. MAYBE HE'S COME BACK FOR *PAUL.*

I *CAN'T* LET HIM ESCAPE. I'VE GOT TO *DO* SOMETHING ABOUT THAT PLANE...

KLIK
KLIK
KLIK

BRAKKA!
BRAKKA!

THE CIA MUST BE *CLOSE*. BUT THEY'LL NEVER CATCH DREVIN *BEFORE* HE REACHES THAT PLANE...

ALEX...

WE **LOST** DREVIN. WHERE IS HE?

UM... IN THAT **CESSNA.**

DAMMIT! HOW COULD YOU LET HIM —

— GET AWAY...? **WHAT THE HELL?**

I DIDN'T HAVE MUCH **TIME.** DREVIN WOULD HAVE NOTICED IF I'D SECURED THE PLANE TO THE **JETTY** ... BUT I GUESSED HE **WOULDN'T** NOTICE **KAYAKS** TIED TO THE FLOATS. I THOUGHT IT WOULD SLOW HIM DOWN...

WELL, IT **DIDN'T!** AND THAT PLANE HAS A MOUNTED **GUN...**

HE'S *TURNING* TO MAKE A SECOND PASS! GET EVERYONE *INSIDE* THE HOUSE!

NO, *WAIT*! LOOK, HE HASN'T NOTICED THE KAYAKS...

...THEY'RE *CAUGHT* IN THE *TREES*!

...GET DOWN!

WHAT...?!

BRRRRMMMMM-BRRM-B-B-B-

WELL, UH... THERE *ISN'T* ONE.

YOU SAID YOU WERE *IN CONTROL* OF THE ISLAND!

DREVIN WAS THE *ONLY ONE* WITH THE CODES. WE CAN'T *COMMUNICATE* WITH GABRIEL 7, AND THAT MEANS WE *CAN'T* BRING IT BACK OR DIVERT IT.

IN LESS THAN THREE HOURS, GABRIEL 7 WILL *DOCK* WITH ARK ANGEL. THE BOMB IS ON A *TIMER*. IT'S ALL GOING TO HAPPEN EXACTLY AS DREVIN PLANNED.

UNLESS, THAT IS...

UNLESS WHAT?

ALEX, I'M REALLY SORRY...

BUT WE NEED YOUR *HELP* AGAIN.

YOU'VE **GOT** TO BE JOKING.

NO JOKE, ALEX. THE **ONLY** WAY TO STOP THE BOMB IS TO SEND SOMEONE UP INTO SPACE **AFTER** IT.

GABRIEL 7 WILL DOCK WITH ARK ANGEL AT HALF PAST TWO. DREVIN TOLD YOU THE BOMB WILL **EXPLODE** TWO HOURS LATER, YES?

HALF PAST FOUR. THAT'S WHAT HE SAID.

BUT DREVIN HAS **LOCKED DOWN** THE ENTIRE COMPUTER SYSTEM CONTROLLING IT. IT WOULD TAKE **DAYS** TO HACK INTO THE SYSTEM... AND WE ONLY HAVE **HOURS**.

THE SOLE REMAINING OPTION IS FOR SOMEONE TO *GO UP* AND NEUTRALIZE THE BOMB. EITHER SWITCH IT OFF, *OR* MOVE IT FROM ITS DOCKING POINT.

RIGHT NOW IT'S SET TO EXPLODE AT THE *EDGE*. CORRECT, PROFESSOR?

YES! THE VERY EDGE! THAT'S WHAT MR DREVIN INSISTED.

AN EXPLOSION THERE WILL LEAVE MOST OF ARK ANGEL *INTACT* BUT SEND THE REST *SPINNING* OUT OF ORBIT... AND DOWN ON WASHINGTON.

BUT IF WE CAN MOVE THE BOMB TO THE *CENTRE* INSTEAD, THE EXPLOSION WILL *VAPORIZE* THE WHOLE STATION.

YOU KEEP SAYING *"WE"*. BUT ACTUALLY, YOU MEAN *ME*.

I'M SORRY, ALEX, BUT YOU'RE THE *ONLY* PERSON HERE WHO CAN RIDE THE *SOYUZ-FREGAT* UP TO THE STATION.

IT'S TRUE! WE PLANNED TO PUT *ARTHUR*, THE APE, INTO SPACE. I MADE ALL THE CALCULATIONS *PERSONALLY*.

THOSE CALCULATIONS RELY ON HIS *HEIGHT* AND *WEIGHT*.

YOU'RE *ABOUT* THE SAME SIZE AS ARTHUR — CLOSE ENOUGH TO BE WITHIN THE MARGIN OF ERROR.

THE REST OF US ARE JUST *TOO BIG*.

THIS WHOLE IDEA IS *INSANE*. BUT THERE'S SOMETHING ELSE, SOMETHING ABOUT THE *PROFESSOR*, THAT'S BUGGING ME. HE CLAIMS HE *DIDN'T KNOW* ABOUT THE PLANS...

ALEX, *PAY ATTENTION!* THIS IS IMPORTANT STUFF THAT YOU *NEED* TO KNOW!

THE BOMB IS CURRENTLY IN GABRIEL 7. IF YOU TAKE IT TO THE *SLEEPING AREA* IN THE HEART OF ARK ANGEL, WASHINGTON WILL BE *SAFE*.

ALL I HAVE TO DO IS *CARRY* IT FROM ONE PLACE TO ANOTHER?

IT WON'T EVEN *WEIGH* ANYTHING. *ZERO GRAVITY*, YOU SEE!

I THOUGHT *MOST* KIDS WOULD GIVE THEIR RIGHT ARM TO GO INTO SPACE. DIDN'T YOU EVER *DREAM* OF BECOMING AN *ASTRONAUT*?

ACTUALLY, I ALWAYS WANTED TO BE A *TRAIN DRIVER*.

YOU'RE *SURE* YOU CAN GET HIM THERE SAFELY, PROFESSOR?

OF COURSE! HE WILL FOLLOW A TRAJECTORY THAT *EXACTLY* MATCHES THE INCLINATION OF ARK ANGEL.

ALL SET, ALEX?

I'D FEEL *A LOT* BETTER IF I WAS WEARING A *PROPER* SPACE SUIT.

THERE IS NO NEED. YOU WILL BE INSIDE A *SEALED CAPSULE* AT ALL TIMES. IT IS *PERFECTLY* SAFE!

REMEMBER *NOT* TO LOOK DIRECTLY AT THE SUN, IT'LL *BLIND* YOU...

THE BOMB IS INSIDE THE *OBSERVATION MODULE* OF GABRIEL 7...

DON'T WASTE TIME. MOVE THE BOMB AND GET RIGHT BACK INSIDE THE SOYUZ *RE-ENTRY MODULE*...

T MINUS TWENTY SECONDS.

T MINUS TEN.

T MINUS FIVE... FOUR... THREE... TWO... ONE.

IT'S HARD TO BELIEVE WE'RE BOTH MOVING AT *SEVENTEEN THOUSAND* MILES PER HOUR...

>KLINK<

...AND I GUESS THAT'S *IT.* I'M DOCKED.

WOW.

SZSZSZSZSZSZSZSZ

ER... *HELLO?* ALEX TO CONTROL...?

DAMN. I MUST BE OUT OF *RANGE,* OR MAYBE EVEN ON THE WRONG SIDE OF THE EARTH. NEVER MIND, I *KNOW* WHAT I HAVE TO DO...

OWWWWW! AND GETTING USED TO ZERO-G WOULD BE A START!

KLANG!!

OK, TRY AGAIN. REMEMBER TO MOVE *SLOWLY.*

JUST A VERY *GENTLE* PUSH...

...IS *ALL* IT SHOULD TAKE...

...TO GET ME *MOVING.*

ARK ANGEL MAY CALL ITSELF A *HOTEL,* BUT IT'S STILL A SPACE STATION. TALK ABOUT *CRAMPED!*

YOWWW! OR IT MIGHT FACE DIRECTLY INTO THE SUN!

YOU *IDIOT*, ALEX. THE PROFESSOR *SAID* THE SUN COULD BLIND YOU.

THIS IS THE *HEART* OF ARK ANGEL. THE DINING ROOM, LIVING ROOM, GYM, EVEN BATHROOMS, ALL NEXT TO ONE ANOTHER. *GABRIEL 7* WILL HAVE DOCKED AT THE FAR END...

...OH, NO.

...AND THEN PROFESSOR SING WOULD SEND THE SOYUZ UP TO *COLLECT* HIM. NO WONDER SING LOOKED *NERVOUS*! I BET THERE WERE ORDERS TO *KILL* HIM IF HE DIDN'T SEND THE ROCKET.

BUT NOW THERE ARE *TWO* OF US, AND ONLY ONE SEAT BACK DOWN. IT'S ME OR HIM... AND KASPAR LOOKS A *LOT* MORE COMFORTABLE IN ZERO-G THAN ME!

ONLY *ONE* CHANCE TO GET THIS MOVE RIGHT!

HA! NO MATTER HOW GOOD YOU ARE IN ZERO-G, YOU CAN'T *CHANGE DIRECTION* MID-AIR!

YOWWWW!

THAT WAS TOO CLOSE. ANOTHER CENTIMETRE, AND IT WOULD HAVE DRAWN *BLOOD!*

THIS MUST BE THE GYM... BUT THERE'S *NOTHING* I CAN USE AS A WEAPON! WHERE ARE THE *WEIGHTS?!*

DUH. YOU FOOL, ALEX. WHAT GOOD ARE WEIGHTS IN *SPACE?*

KASPAR! YOU'VE GOT TO UNDERSTAND, IT'S OVER. THERE'S NO POINT IN *FIGHTING.*

DREVIN'S DEAD. THE *CIA* IS IN CONTROL OF FLAMINGO BAY.

OOF!

RRRRRGGGHH!

BASIC PHYSICS, ALEX. FOR EVERY *ACTION* THERE'S AN EQUAL AND OPPOSITE *REACTION*... MEANING, DON'T THROW THINGS SO *HARD!*

NNNGH! TOO STRONG... NO WEAPONS... I'M *BLACKING OUT*...!

WAIT... ANOTHER SHUTTER RELEASE...

IT'S SO **SMALL**... AND YET EVERY HUMAN, ANIMAL AND PLANT THAT'S **EVER** LIVED, LIVED ON THAT TINY BALL OF ROCK.

I WAS WRONG. THE **REAL** MIRACLE IS DOWN THERE AND ALL THE **LIFE** IT GIVES. ARK ANGEL'S A STERILE, **DEAD** PLACE.

ALEX, THIS IS **TAMARA**. WE'RE READING **ACTIVITY** IN THE SOYUZ **RE-ENTRY MODULE**. WHAT'S YOUR STATUS?

GOOD RIDDANCE.

PROFESSOR SING **LIED** TO US. **KASPAR** WAS HERE.

I'VE **MOVED** THE BOMB, BUT IT'S STILL ACTIVE. GET ME **OUT** OF HERE!

YOU GOT IT.